China C

Traditional mining m

C000148326

Charles Thurlow

Tor Mark Press • Redruth

The Tor Mark series

Folklore

Classic Cornish ghost stories
Classic Devon ghost stories
Classic West Country ghost stories
Cornish fairies
Cornish folklore
Cornish legends
Customs and superstitions from
  Cornish folklore
Demons, ghosts and spectres in
  Cornish folklore
Devonshire customs and
  superstitions
Devonshire legends
Down 'long weth we
The Pixy Book

Other titles

Charlestown
China clay
Classic Cornish anecdotes
Cornish fishing industry
Cornish mining – at surface
Cornish mining – underground
Cornish mining industry
Cornish recipes
Cornish saints
Cornwall in camera
Cornwall's early lifeboats
Cornwall's engine houses
Cornwall's railways
Devonshire jokes and stories
Do you know Cornwall?
Exploring Cornwall with your car
Harry Carter – Cornish smuggler
Houses, castles and gardens
  in Cornwall
Introducing Cornwall
King Arthur – man or myth?
Lost ports of Cornwall
Old Cornwall – in pictures
Shipwrecks around Land's End
Shipwrecks around the Lizard
Shipwrecks around Mounts Bay
Shipwrecks - Falmouth to Looe
South-east Cornwall
The story of Cornwall
The story of the Cornish language
The story of St Ives
The story of Truro Cathedral
Tales of the Cornish fishermen
Tales of the Cornish miners
Tales of the Cornish smugglers
Tales of the Cornish wreckers
Twelve walks on the Lizard

Tor Mark Press, United Downs Industrial Estate, St Day,
Redruth, Cornwall, TR16 5HY
First published 1990
Second edition 1996
© Tor Mark Press, 1990, 1996
ISBN 0-85025-358-6

Acknowledgements
All the photographs in this book are reproduced by kind permission of
ECC plc, except those on pages 11 and 12 and the cover illustration
(Harold Harvey's 'The Clay Pit', 1923) which are reproduced by kind
permission of the Royal Cornwall Museum.

Printed in Great Britain by Burstwick Print & Publicity Services, Hull

Introduction

China clay was formed in Cornwall and Devon by the gradual decomposition over millions of years of some of the granite rock which runs from Dartmoor to Land's End. It was discovered in the mid-eighteenth century by a Plymouth chemist called William Cookworthy, who was looking for one of the secret ingredients which the Chinese had used for a thousand years to make porcelain, and which had been known in Meissen, Saxony, since about 1710.

The method of winning china clay did not change much from the eighteenth century to the early twentieth century. Many small companies were at work. The photographs in this book date from the last quarter of the nineteenth century and the first quarter of the twentieth, before amalgamations and large scale operation changed the industry. Even today, the principles remain the same: removing the overburden, breaking up the clay face using water, separating the clay slurry from sands by gradual refinement in a series of settling processes, drying the clay and then shipping it.

Removing the overburden

The surface is covered with soil and vegetation which discolours the upper level of the china clay. Before working could take place, this material, known as 'overburden' or 'overburthen', had to be removed and discarded. Teams of men were employed to remove overburden using picks and shovels. The picks were a local type with a single chisel point, known as dubbers.

Overburden was tipped into small wooden rail waggons, which were pushed by hand towards a tip away from the clay working or, at larger pits, pulled in trains by horses.

Breaking up the clay face

Decomposed granite contains very fine particles of china clay together with hard gritty sands called mica and quartz. Water was used to separate these constituents and carry them in a stream to the bottom of the pit. The simplest way of doing this, used for over a hundred years, was to divert a stream over the rock face, where men called breakers used dubbers and other tools to break up the decomposed granite, as shown in the picture on the left.

By the end of the nineteenth century, as pits deepened, water was piped from the surface through hoses with narrow nozzles to wash the clay. A hoseman directed the jet of water onto the clay face; the need for breakers was gradually reduced as hoses came into general use and water pressures were increased by pumping.

Separating clay from sand

In the following processes, the china clay was separated from the associated sands in settling tanks. Minerals mixed up in water are called a suspension – mud in a muddy stream is 'in suspension'. In any suspension the coarser particles, such as mica and quartz, settle faster than the finer particles, such as china clay. If the liquid can be moved on after the mica and quartz have settled, but before the fine clay has time to do so, the clay can be isolated.

In the bottom of the pit, the clay-bearing stream passed through wide channels where the coarse sand settled and was held back whilst the stream carrying fine sand and clay was pumped as slurry to the surface. The photograph below shows the timber structure used to trap the sand. On the right of the structure is a vertical wooden pipe, square in section, called a button hole launder; it leads to the pumps.

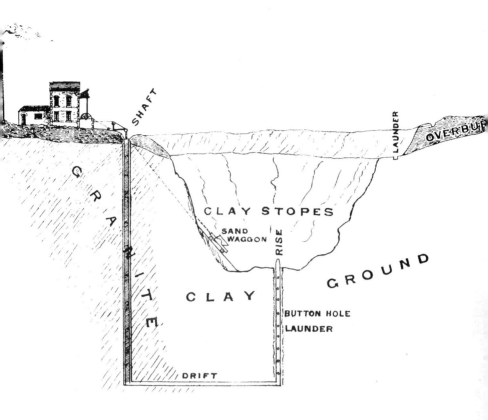

The following labels appear in the diagram: SHAFT, LAUNDER, OVERBUR, CLAY STOPES, SAND WAGGON, RISE, GROUND, CLAY, BUTTON HOLE LAUNDER, DRIFT, GRANITE

Sometimes china clay and fine sand, in suspension with water from a clay pit, could be drained by a tunnel called an adit, cut through the hillside. As pits grew deeper, adits were replaced by pumps.

The diagram above, published in 1880, shows the general arrangement of a china clay pit. A shaft, containing a pump, was sunk alongside the pit. The mining work was carried out by men experienced in Cornish mining, and the beam engine was similar to the engines used at local tin mines.

From the bottom of the shaft a horizontal tunnel called a level or drift connected with a button hole launder. The button hole launder had a series of circular holes at intervals, sealed by pieces of wood called buttons nailed over them. As the pit deepened, buttons were removed to allow the slurry, carrying the china clay and fine sand, to enter the launder, flow along the level to the foot of the shaft and be pumped up to the surface.

This beam engine at a works near Whitemoor was used to pump china clay. Similar beam engines are preserved by the National Trust at Pool near Redruth and are well worth visiting. The beam seen projecting from the engine house, above the platform, moved up and down by the action of steam on a large piston in a cylinder inside the house. The beam raised and lowered a plunger which pushed the slurry through valves at the base of the shaft into a pipe, which came up the shaft and discharged the slurry into a wooden trough also called a launder; the launder can be seen in the photograph, raised well above the ground to allow gravity feed to the next stage of processing.

The picture opposite shows the engine house at Goonvean Pit near St Dennis. Over the top of the pump are the shear legs and pulley used to lower and raise the pipework when pumps were installed or replaced.

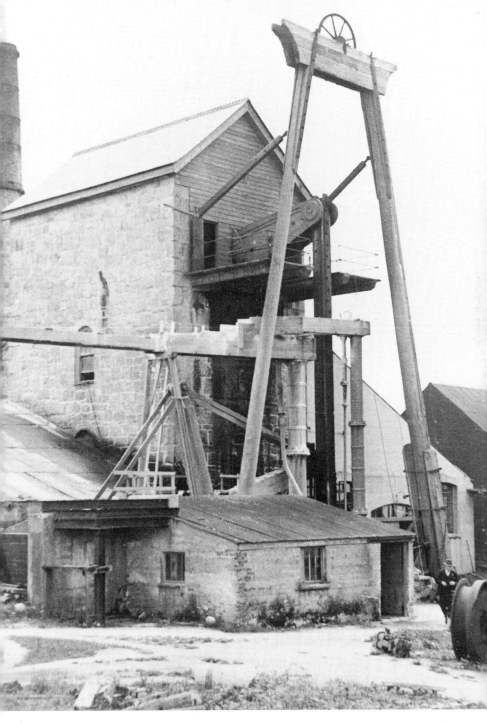

Water was in use to power the pumps before steam engines, and some water wheels survived, such as this one which can be seen working at the Wheal Martyn China Clay Heritage Centre.

In this general view of a clay pit around 1920, the clay stream is being directed to the button hole launder, to the right of the double incline railway. The remains of an abandoned adit (looking like a cave in the rock face) can be seen on the extreme right. At one time this adit had been used to drain from the pit china clay and fine sand in suspension.

Removal of sand and rock

Sand which had settled in pits was loaded into waggons using triangular-bladed shovels. The waggons were then pushed a short distance to the foot of the incline railway.

Waggons on the incline railway were adapted for use at an angle, and were called skips – the word used in the mines. The skip was hoisted to the top of the incline by a wire rope wound on a horizontal drum, powered by a horse or a water wheel in the early days of clay working and later by a rotative Cornish beam engine. At the top, the skip was tipped to empty it and then returned to the bottom.

The china clay district was sometimes referred to as the Cornish Alps because of the proliferation of inclined tips, largely composed of white quartz sand, which can look very like snow when seen from a distance, particularly in evening sunshine. The large number of tips resulted from the many small companies working independently. Some of the tips in this scene have been superseded by newer tips as the pits deepened and more tipping space was required.

China clay pits contain a proportion of granite which has not decomposed, as well as veins of other minerals such as tourmaline and quartz which are too hard to be broken up and transported by water. This rocky material, known as stent, had to be removed from working faces. In the top photograph opposite, one working face is being cleared of stent while washing continues in an adjacent area. The lower photograph shows a detail from a similar scene.

Waggon loads of stent were pushed to a point where they could be transferred into a skip on the incline railway.

Settling out fine sand

In the early days of the industry, china slurry which had been pumped from the pit was further refined by passing through two or three shallow rectangular pits walled with local stone. These were called drags. The object was to settle out fine sands from the china clay in a simple, but inefficient, process.

In the mid-nineteenth century, the refining of slurry was improved. One drag pit was retained, but a set of long narrow channels replaced the other drags. These channels were only a few inches deep and the rate of flow through them could be precisely controlled by flaps to ensure that all fine sands in the slurry were settled out. Because the fine sand contained a good deal of a flaky material called mica, these channels were called micas.

At intervals the fine sands were cleared out of the channels by the 'mica man' who used a large hoe shaped to fit the channel. The hoe was known as a shiver, pronounced shyver.

Underneath the channels of the mica drags were a system of drains which were plugged when the drags were in use. To clear the channels the plugs were removed and fine sand was discharged down the drains into the local rivers, which used to be known as 'white rivers' because the residue contained some china clay.

Thickening and drying

China clay which had been refined in the drags flowed on as a milky white liquid into large rectangular or circular pits up to ten feet in depth, usually constructed with stone walls and floors. The clay slowly settled and clear water was run off through a launder on one side of the tank. This was called a pin-hole launder, as the holes were plugged with wooden 'pins'. When the clay had thickened to a creamy consistency, it flowed out through a pipe running underneath the pit to a second set of tanks where further thickening took place.

During the first century or so of china clay production, the second stage, thickening, took place in shallow tanks called sun pans and drying took place in open sheds called air dries. In the sun pans, clay was allowed to thicken on a thin layer of sand placed in the pan. Water was run off until solid blocks of clay could be cut out. In the earliest days these blocks were dried in the open air but later on they were stacked or placed in a covered building with open sides called an air dry.

The photograph shows the works manager – known as the Captain, as were
the managers in Cornish mines – standing between two sun pans in front
of an air dry.

In this air dry the clay is in irregularly shaped lumps, and is probably a low grade of clay. The drying process took many months in the damp Cornish winters. After drying, clay in this dry was stockpiled at one side of the building.

The better grades of china clay from air dries were scraped clean after drying to remove sand and any mould. The task was carried out by women using triangular-bladed scrapers as shown in this posed photograph. After being scraped, the blocks of clay were stacked on one side of the dry.

In the mid-nineteenth century the slow process of sun pan thickening and air drying was gradually replaced by deeper thickening tanks and drying on long floors heated by coal fires. The dries were roofed and built alongside settling tanks.

The outer tanks were filled with china clay from settling pits, which was allowed to thicken until most of the clay was the consistency of butter. Clear water from the top of the tanks was tapped off through pin holes in the boards that closed the access hatch. In the central tank in this photograph, thickened clay is being dug out and loaded into waggons before being transferred onto the drying floor. The open hatch can be seen.

Inside the dry, the waggon of clay has been run onto a bridge which can travel the whole length of the dry on a set of rails. The clay was tipped evenly over the floor of the dry.

The floor, called a pan, consisted of large bricks or tiles resting on a series of brick walls built to conduct heat from coal fires under the tiles to a tall chimney stack at the far end of the dry. Clay placed on the floor was cut while it was still damp into lumps convenient for later handling. Drying took from one to five days, depending on whether the clay was at the hot end close to the fires, or at the chimney end which was cooler.

Beside the pan was a storage area or 'linhay' for dried china clay.

Transport

China clay often began its journey to the customer in horse drawn waggons which carried three or four tons of clay to the local ports, for shipment to destinations all over Britain, as well as abroad. The most direct route to the ports took these waggons through the main street of St Austell, and they required the help of extra horses on the steep hills.

Dried china clay was often transshipped several times between waggons, ships or trains, so that robust packaging was needed to avoid damage. Much clay was sold in casks such as these which contained about five hundredweights (approximately 250 kg) of clay. Special tamping tools and mallets were used in the packing and closing of casks.

Manufacture of these casks provided work for several cooperages in the clay district. Much of the timber was imported from the Baltic on vessels which came to collect the clay. The use of casks began to decline by the end of the nineteenth century in favour of jute sacks.

From the mid 1850s a network of railway lines developed in the china clay area. Many china clay producers owned their own rail trucks to ensure fast transport to their customers. Clay could be loaded direct from the linhay on to the trucks, with just a wooden plank used to bridge the gap. This train is almost loaded and some trucks are being sheeted.

Par Harbour was built in the 1850s to serve local mines and stone quarries, but china clay soon became the major export.

Fowey is a natural sheltered deep water anchorage which was connected to Par by rail in 1874, enabling china clay to be loaded. Horses were used to shunt waggons via a turntable to the steam cranes which then transferred a pair of casks at a time.

Par and Fowey are still in use; today the industry exports two million tons of china clay each year through these ports. Most of this clay is used by the paper industry. Some is used as a filler with wood pulp to make white paper. The finest clays are used as a coating to add gloss to white paper.

Other industries using china clay are ceramics, rubber, paint and plastics.

Wheal Martyn

The history of china clay production is best studied at the Wheal Martyn China Clay Heritage Centre, Carthew, just north of St Austell on B3274. Here there are permanent indoor displays and a 'history trail' round many of the features described in this book, as well as a nature trail, a spectacular view of a modern working pit and facilities for children. It is open daily from Easter to October.